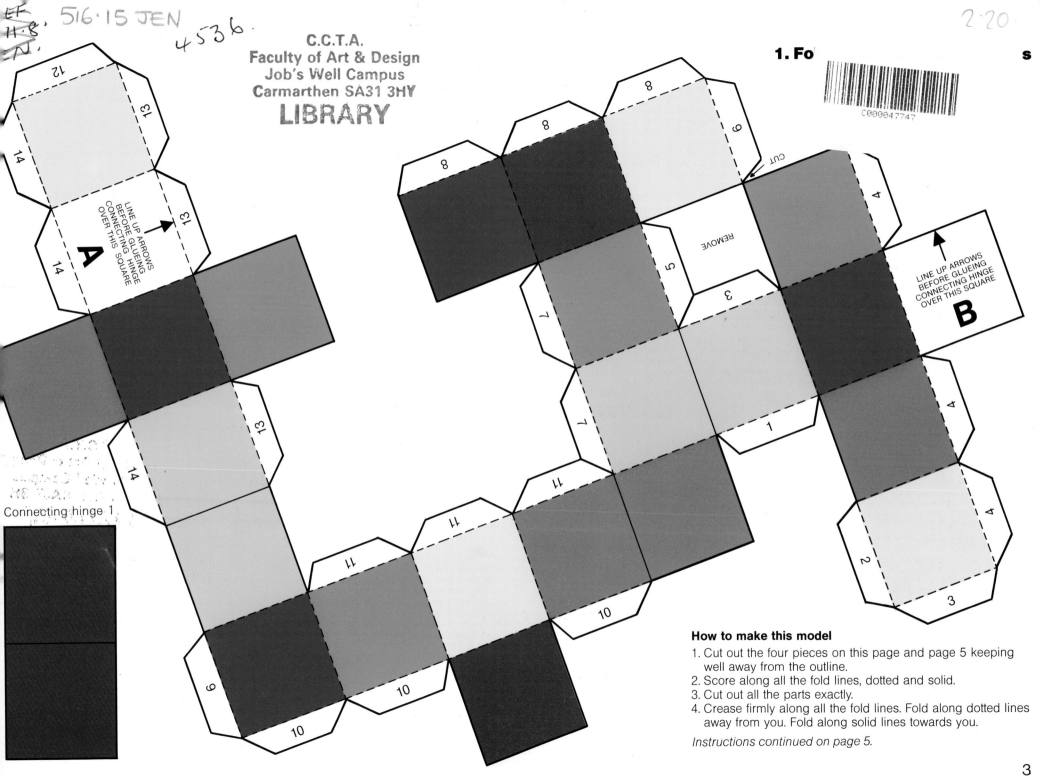

1. Fo   s

LINE UP ARROWS
BEFORE GLUEING
CONNECTING HINGE
OVER THIS SQUARE

A

Connecting hinge 1

REMOVE

CUT

LINE UP ARROWS
BEFORE GLUEING
CONNECTING HINGE
OVER THIS SQUARE

B

How to make this model
1. Cut out the four pieces on this page and page 5 keeping well away from the outline.
2. Score along all the fold lines, dotted and solid.
3. Cut out all the parts exactly.
4. Crease firmly along all the fold lines. Fold along dotted lines away from you. Fold along solid lines towards you.

Instructions continued on page 5.

3

5

3

4

4

7

4

7

13

13

14

2

13

6

14

1

14

8

12

11

8

11

9

8

11

A

10

10

10

A

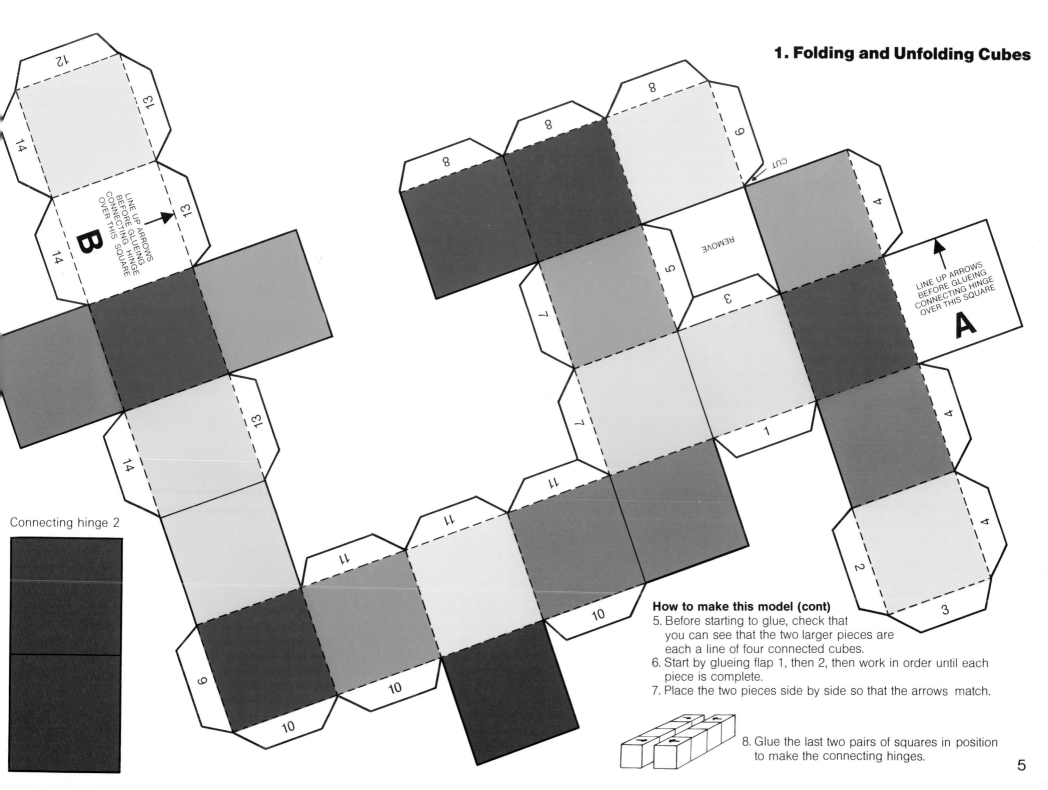

LINE UP ARROWS
BEFORE GLUEING
CONNECTING HINGE
OVER THIS SQUARE

B

LINE UP ARROWS
BEFORE GLUEING
CONNECTING HINGE
OVER THIS SQUARE

A

REMOVE

CUT

Connecting hinge 2

How to make this model (cont)

5. Before starting to glue, check that
   you can see that the two larger pieces are
   each a line of four connected cubes.
6. Start by glueing flap 1, then 2, then work in order until each
   piece is complete.
7. Place the two pieces side by side so that the arrows match.

8. Glue the last two pairs of squares in position
   to make the connecting hinges.

5

3

5

3

7

4

4

7

13

13

4

14

2

6

13

14

1

14

8

12

11

8

11

9

11

8

10

B

10

10

10

B

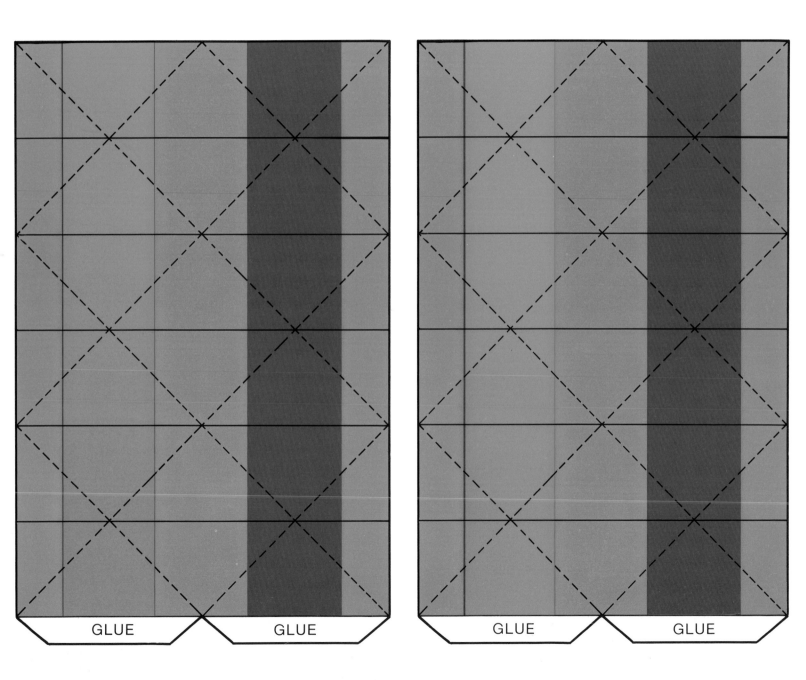

2. The Polyhedra Flower

HOW TO MAKE THIS MODEL.

1. Cut out both pieces keeping well away from the outline.
2. Score along all fold lines, dotted and solid.
3. Cut out the two shapes precisely.
4. Fold and crease cleanly. Fold along dotted lines away from you. Fold along solid lines towards you.
5. Glue the flaps to make a single cylinder with the multi-colour outside.
6. Fold each crease the way it should go to complete your polyhedra flower.

For more information about the Polyhedra flower, see page 2 of the minibook.

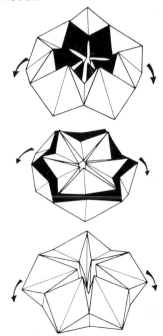

3. Shapes of Constant Width

HOW TO MAKE THESE MODELS.

1. Cut out all the parts keeping well away from the outline.
2. Score along the lines marked — — — — and —·—·—·—
3. Cut out all the parts precisely.

TO MAKE THE ROLLING FRAME.

1. Fold along the dotted line away from you and along the lines marked —·—·—·— towards you.
2. Crease firmly and then glue together to make the frame.

TO MAKE THE THREE ARC ROLLER

1. Fold away from you along the dotted lines.
2. Glue the flaps to make a triangular prism.
3. Glue each of the shapes marked A to a side to make the roller.

For information about shapes of constant width, see page 3 of the minibook.

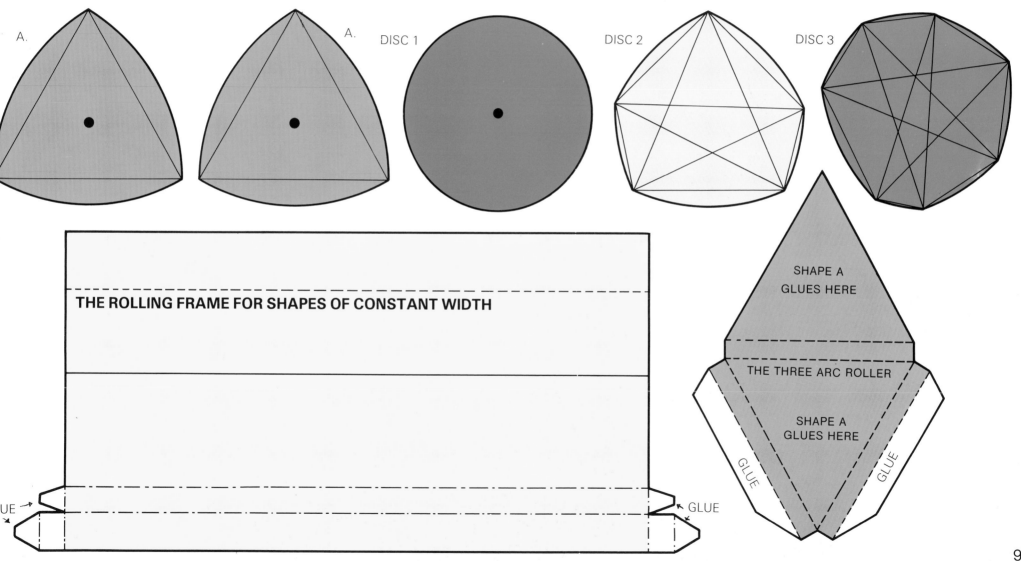

A.

A.

DISC 1

DISC 2

DISC 3

THE ROLLING FRAME FOR SHAPES OF CONSTANT WIDTH

GLUE

GLUE

SHAPE A
GLUES HERE

THE THREE ARC ROLLER

SHAPE A
GLUES HERE

GLUE

GLUE

A   A   A

4. Möbius Strips

For the properties of each model and details of the "ham sandwich" test see page 4 of the minibook.

HOW TO MAKE THESE MODELS.

1. Cut out all four pieces keeping well away from the outlines.
2. Score along the dotted central line of each of the Möbius strips.
3. Cut out each outline precisely.
4. Fold each strip away from you and crease firmly so that they match back to back.
5. Spread glue evenly inside the fold and then press tightly.
6. Form a loop, giving each a half twist. The unprinted flap glues to the grey tone, giving a strip totally coloured on both sides.

MODEL 1

SIDE BECAUSE THIS WRITING CONTINUES RIGHT ROUND IT SHOWING CLEARLY THAT

A MÖBIUS STRIP ONLY HAS ONE SIDE. YOU CAN TELL THAT IT ONLY HAS ONE

MODEL 2

MÖBIUS STRIP WHICH HAS TWO SIDES, TWO EDGES AND A DOUBLE TWIST WHICH IS

THE RESULT OF CUTTING A ONE SIDED MÖBIUS STRIP IN HALF GIVING A NEW

MODEL 3

this is the filling for the 'ham sandwich' test

HAS TWO SIDES AND TWO EDGES AND ALSO HAS A DOUBLE TWIST

CUTTING A ONE SIDED MÖBIUS STRIP IN THREE GIVES THIS ONE SIDED

CUTTING A ONE SIDED MÖBIUS STRIP IN THREE GIVES THIS LOOP WHICH

LOOP WHICH ONLY HAS ONE EDGE, THE ONE ABOVE THIS WRITING

5. The Klein Cube

A surface with only one side and no boundaries

HOW TO MAKE THIS MODEL.

1. Cut out the three pieces on this page and on page 15, keeping well away from the outline.

2. Score along all the fold lines, then cut out precisely. At dotted lines fold away from you. At solid lines fold towards you. Crease each fold firmly.

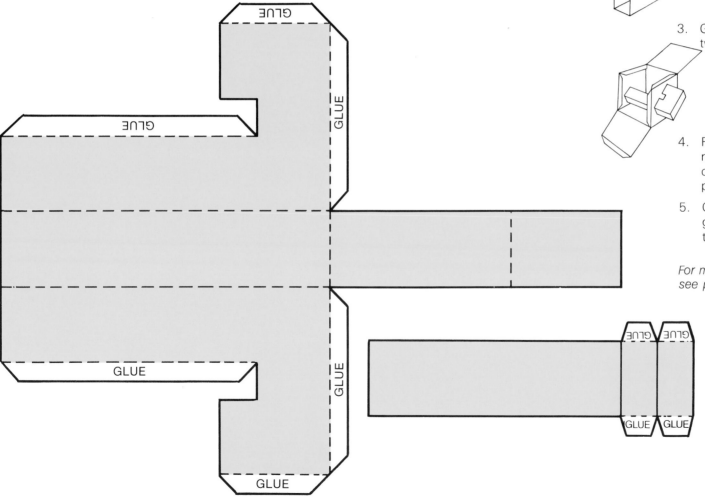

3. Glue together the central tube using the two smaller pieces.

4. Fold the cube into shape but it is best not to glue the side flaps until the central tube is in position and glued into place.

5. Glue the side flaps of the cube. Do not glue the lid down. It is more interesting to be able to look inside.

For more information about the Klein cube, see pages 4 and 5 of the minibook.

GLUE

GLUE

GLUE

GLUE

GLUE

GLUE

GLUE

GLUE

GLUE

GLUE

GLUE

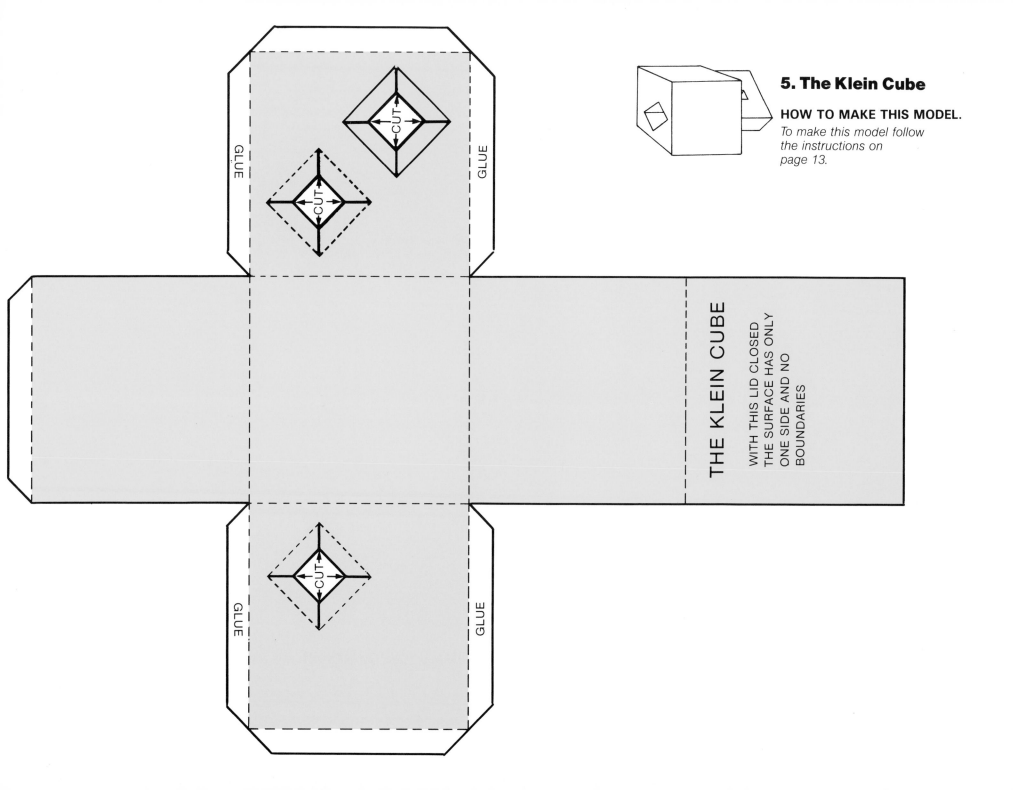

GLUE

GLUE

CUT

CUT

CUT

CUT

GLUE

GLUE

THE KLEIN CUBE

WITH THIS LID CLOSED
THE SURFACE HAS ONLY
ONE SIDE AND NO
BOUNDARIES

5. The Klein Cube

HOW TO MAKE THIS MODEL.

*To make this model follow
the instructions on
page 13.*

Mathematical
Curiosities 1

Some Curious Mathematical Ideas

Suggested by this collection of models

Book 1

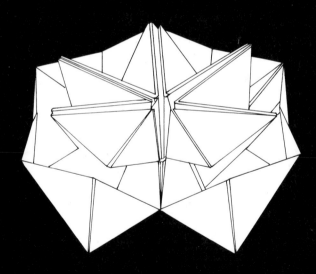

Tarquin
Publications

0 906212 13 8

Gerald Jenkins   **Anne Wild**

See inside the front cover for instructions on how to make the minibook.

Curious models . . .

1. Folding and Unfolding Cubes
2. The Polyhedra Flower
3. Shapes of Constant Width
4. Möbius Strips
5. The Klein Cube
6. The Double-sided Magic Square Puzzle
7. The Diabolic Frame
8. The Double Helix
9. Hexaflexagons

If you have enjoyed making these models, then there are other Tarquin books which may interest you. In particular, there are two more books in this series. At present there are three different series of books of mathematical shapes to cut out and make.

Make Shapes Series   **Books 1, 2, 3**
Mathematical Curiosities Series **Books 1, 2, 3**
Tarquin Polyhedra Series   **Books 1, 2, 3**

Tarquin books are available from Bookshops, Toy Shops, Art/Craft Shops and in case of difficulty directly by post from the publishers.

For an up-to-date catalogue, please write to Tarquin Publications, Stradbroke, Diss, Norfolk IP21 5JP England.

9. Hexaflexagons

A Hexaflexagon is a curious assembly of equilateral triangles which are folded together to make a hexagonal shape. By flexing along certain axes, hidden faces appear. If all the faces are coloured, you can get some dramatic colour changes, which occur in a cyclic fashion.

Not only do new triangles flex into view, they also change in orientation. The red triangles for instance are not in the same orientation if you have come from yellow as if you have come from blue. It is easy to test this by marking small arrows on the red, flexing it out of sight, and then making it reappear from both sides.

A more amusing way of demonstrating this property is to draw faces on the faces! Only by flexing a face into view while facing a certain face will you get a face you can recognise!

The net for a simple hexaflagon is not difficult to draw and it is interesting to make some more on plain paper and then to experiement by designing suitable patterns for them.

The Colour Addition Hexaflexagon

You are strongly advised to make up the simpler hexaflexagons first.

This hexaflexagon flexes to give three primary colours red, blue, yellow just like its simpler relative. The axes which have to be flexed to give this primary circuit are marked by a double P - printed P̱, meaning PRIMARY.

Beyond that, there is also a set of secondary colours which can be flexed into view, giving the result of adding the two visible primary colours together. This is brought about by flexing along the axes, marked by a double A, printed A̱, meaning ADD.

red + yellow = orange: yellow + blue = green: blue + red = purple. Once a secondary colour is obtained, you will notice that it is not possible to pass from it to another secondary colour. However the visible colours can be substracted by flexing along the axes marked with a doubles printed S̱, meaning SUBTRACT.

green − blue = yellow: orange − red = yellow: purple − blue = red:
green − yellow = blue: orange − yellow = red: purple − red = blue.

Once you have found a secondary colour, access to the primary circuit is partly blocked. It can never be obtained by flexing while facing the secondary colour, and if you turn it over so as to face the primary colour only one set of axes will actually flex, although the printing suggests that both will. The flex which does work brings you back into the primary circuit and from there the other secondary colours can be reached.

8

1

2

3

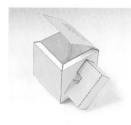

4

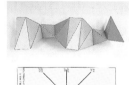

5

6

7

8

9

Curious mathematical ideas . . .

1

See inside the front cover for instructions on how to make the minibook.

19

1. Folding and Unfolding Cubes

Eight small cubes joined together in a curious way so that they will fold to make a larger cube or a 4 x 2 x 1 cuboid, each of which unfolds to make the other and in doing so giving a continuously changing pattern of colours.

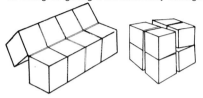

Investigation.
1. The larger faces of the cuboid are all the same colour. Can all six colours be placed there?
2. How many different cuboids can be made?
3. How many different cubes can be made?
4. Try making another set of eight separate cubes and then linking them together with transparent tape. You will find that certain other ways of linking them leads to other curious effects.

2. The Polyhedra Flower

To make the polyhedra flower bloom, hold it gently in the fingers. The centre inside will rise and open out, then turn over and become the outside only to reappear as the sequence continues without end. Who could have guessed that right angled isosceles triangles could behave like this!

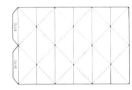

The net is given here for you to make more polyhedra flowers, which you can decorate yourself. Draw it on plain paper, preferably a strong cartridge. All the angles are either 45° or 90° and you need two identical pieces.

7. The Diabolic Frame

1	8	10	15
14	11	5	4
7	2	16	9
12	13	3	6

While investigating the properties of a diabolic square, you may also have noticed that the groups of four on opposite sides of the square also add up to 34. This means that if a diabolic square is wrapped round to make a three dimensional model, then the model will have yet more properties.

This is exactly what has been done to make the Diabolic Frame model, in fact using these numbers.
Try adding up the four numbers on the inside, or on the outside, or on each face or of each colour, or the numbers meeting at the corner on the inside, or at each corner on the outside. Try starting anywhere and spiralling upwards or downwards. In every case the total is 34. If you search further you will find yet more totals of 34.
If you would like to make a diabolic frame yourself, use the other numbers on page 6 – or the solution to either side when you have found it – or discover some more yourself – there are still 44 left to find!

8. The Double Helix

This double helix, reminiscent of the DNA molecule, is constructed from a linked series of isosceles tetrahedra. Note how all the lines which join one tetrahedron to the next are in parallel planes which are perpendicular to the axis, and that each one is rotated relative to its neighbours by 45°. It is easy to check this by placing the 'rotation protractor' against each line in turn down its length. Note also that each leg of the spiral makes 45° with the axis.

After four tetrahedra the total rotation is 180°, and thus the fifth tetrahedron is parallel to the first. The sequence of colours brings out this relationship. To complete one turn and a total of 360° takes eight tetrahedra exactly. In a DNA molecule the sequence would continue for hundreds or thousands of turns.
It is interesting to construct another double helix of different rotation. It is not difficult to calculate the angle of the isosceles triangles required. If x is the base angle of the isosceles triangle which makes the net, then the value of x for a given angle of rotation y is given by

$$\cos x = \frac{\sqrt{2} \sin \frac{y}{2}}{2}$$

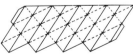

The chain of tetrahedra can be made as long as you wish.

The net of 8 linked tetrahedra.

6. The Double-sided Magic Square Puzzle

Magic squares have exerted a considerable fascination over people for hundreds of years and in former times were given an almost mystical significance. Even today, with a much greater understanding of their construction, they still arouse in most people a feeling of wonder that such patterns could exist. The simplest magic square is a 3 x 3 array, using the consecutive numbers 1 to 9.

To get the total place the numbers consecutively in the array.

You will see that both diagonals add up to 15, which gives the total we require.

After some rearranging we find a magic square where all the rows, columns and diagonals add up to 15.

To find magic squares of order 4, we start the same way.

In this case each diagonal adds up to 34. The formula for a magic square of order n is $\frac{n(n^2+1)}{2}$

A simple reversal of the diagonals gives a magic square of order 4

Note that the groups of 4 at each corner and at the centre each adds up to 34.
There is a special kind of magic square where all the groups of 4 add up to 34 and so do the split diagonals. These are known as DIABOLIC SQUARES.

The problem here is to rearrange the 16 number squares into a 4 x 4 array so that it is a diabolic square on both sides at the same time. To make it more intriguing and susceptible to logical deduction, all the numbers in the same row on one side and in the same column on the other side are in the same colour.

Below are given two diabolic magic squares so that you can see just jow remarkable diabolic squares are.

Check that in each diabolic square, each row, column and diagonal adds up to 34. Note also how every group of 4 also adds up to 34 as do the split diagonals.

Neither of these squares is one of the several possible solutions to the puzzle!

6

3. Shapes of Constant Width

 A circle is a curve of constant radius and also a curve of constant width. Thus it can be used to make a wheel or a roller.

 A circular wheel can be fixed to an axle and used to carry loads. The axle passes through the centre of the wheel. The wheel is possibly the greatest invention there has ever been.

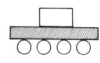 Circular rollers can be used to carry a slab, which is either the load or a platform for the load. As each roller is left behind it must be carried again to the front – but progress is possible even over uneven or relatively soft ground, as the builders of Stonehenge or the Pyramids knew well.

Are there any other such shapes?
There are no other shapes of constant radius, that is with every point on the curve the same distance from the centre – but there are whole families of curves of constant width. These models show a few.

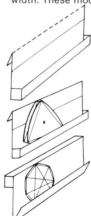 Place the three arc roller inside the frame and roll it back and forth. Note how it always reaches to the top line. Observe also how the centre spot does not travel horizontally, showing that it is not a curve of constant radius. It is interesting to roll a British 50 pence piece also inside the frame, showing that it too has a constant width, a vital property if it is to be used in a slot machine.
The discs are more easily rolled along the fold at the back.
Note that the circle is the only shape with a true centre.

3

See inside the front cover for instructions on how to make the minibook.

4. Möbius Strips

Loops of paper which are given a twist before glueing the ends are called Möbius strips. The simplest Möbius strip is the one which is given a half twist, so that it only has one side.
Other interesting results may be obtained from it by cutting, as these models show.

 Model 1 A simple Möbius strip. Gently pull it through your fingers, reading the words as you do so. The sentence continues on and on, proving that there is only one side. If there were two sides, as many people think when they first see it, there would have to be two separate sentences.

 Model 2 Cutting a simple Möbius strip in half. With a pair of scissors, carefully cut along the centre line of the strip. See how the sides now have different colours, and how one side has words and the other does not. This proves that it has two sides.

 The Ham Sandwich Test
First rearrange the strip so that all the words face each other and you apparently have two simple Möbius strips together. Now take the 'filling' strip and ease it between the two layers. You will find that this can be done 'proving' that the two strips are separate. This is just as a piece of ham protruding all round a sandwich 'proves' that the two slices of bread are separate – or does it? Try it on other people and see what they think.

 Model 3 Cutting a simple Möbius strip in three. With a pair of scissors start to cut along one of the lines of trisection and then carefully follow it until the circuit is complete. Try to guess what will happen before you start. Will the result have one side or two? Will it be twisted?

5. The Klein Cube

A Topological Problem – is there a surface with only one side but no boundaries?
To answer a question like that we must first examine a few shapes to help understand what the problem is.

  A flat sheet of any shape has two sides and a boundary.

  A folded flat sheet still has two sides and a boundary. The new folded edges are not new boundaries. Surfaces like these are topologically equivalent to a flat sheet.

 Joining the two ends of a flat strip together to make a simple loop gives a surface which has two sides and two distinct boundaries.

 Joining the two ends of a flat strip together with a half twist gives a Möbius strip which has one side and one boundary.

So we can see that a 'side' is a region such that every point on it can be joined to any other by a continuous path on the surface which does not cross a boundary. The number of such distinct regions is the number of sides the surface has.
What do surfaces with no boundaries look like?

 A sphere has no boundaries. It has two distinct sides an inside and an outside. It also divides space into two distinct regions.

 A cube is topologically equivalent to a sphere. The edges are not boundaries. It still has two sides.

 A torus is not topologically equivalent to a sphere or cube but it still has no boundaries. It has two sides and divides space into two distinct regions.

 A pair of linked tori has no boundaries. The complete surface has four sides and divides space into three distinct regions.

 Cutting a hole in a cube creates a surface which is different from a cube and which does not divide space into two distinct regions.

However it still has two sides as there is now a boundary around the hole.

This small selection of shapes shows how interesting a world it is that the topologist investigates. Perhaps the most intriguing shape of all is the Klein Bottle, a surface which really does have no boundaries and yet only one side.

A Klein Bottle can be made out of blown glass or rubber, but an interesting variation of it - the Klein Cube, can be made out of paper. Of course the lid is only there so you can see inside - really it should be glued shut.

THE KLEIN BOTTLE

1	2	3	4
5	6	7	8
9	10	11	12
13	14	15	16
14	13	16	15
6	5	8	7
10	9	12	11
2	1	4	3

6. The Double-Sided Magic Square Puzzle

The problem is to rearrange the 16 number squares into a 4 x 4 array so that it is a diabolical square on both sides at the same time. To make it more intriguing and susceptible to logical deduction, all the numbers in the same row on one side and in the same column on the other side are in the same colour.

How to make the pieces of this puzzle

1. Cut it out from the page keeping well away from the outline.
2. Score along the central dotted line.
3. Cut out the outline precisely.
4. Fold away from you along the dotted line and check for an exact match back to back.
5. Spread glue evenly all over the inside of the fold. Press firmly and wait until dry.
6. Cut the square into the 16 smaller numbered squares.

How to make the packet to keep the pieces in.

1. Cut it out from the page keeping well away from the outline.
2. Score along the dotted lines.
3. Cut out precisely.
4. Fold away from you along the dotted lines and glue the two flaps

For more information about this puzzle see page 6 of the minibook.

Make this packet to keep the pieces in.

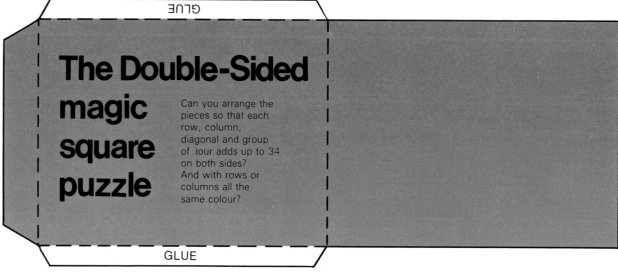

GLUE

The Double-Sided
magic
square
puzzle

Can you arrange the pieces so that each row, column, diagonal and group of four adds up to 34 on both sides? And with rows or columns all the same colour?

GLUE

7. The Diabolic Frame

This three dimensional model is based on the special magic square known as the diabolic square. The properties of the diabolic square are remarkable enough and they are described in the minibook, but the properties of this model are stranger still. All the numbers from 1 to 16 occur once only, but the groups of 4 add up to 34 in virtually every way you could imagine. Try adding up the four numbers on the inside, or on the outside, or on each face, or of each colour, or the numbers meeting at each corner on the inside or each corner on the outside. Try starting anywhere and spiralling upwards or downwards. In every case the total is 34. If you search further you can find yet more totals of 34.

It seems astonishing that even one diabolic frame can be made, but in fact 48 are possible.

For more information about this model see page 7 of the minibook.

HOW TO MAKE THIS MODEL.
1. Cut out the model keeping well away from the outline.
2. Score along all dotted lines.
3. Cut out precisely — removing the centre space and cutting along the thick cut lines as indicated.
4. Fold and crease firmly. When you can see exactly how it fits together, glue the flaps to make the diabolic frame.

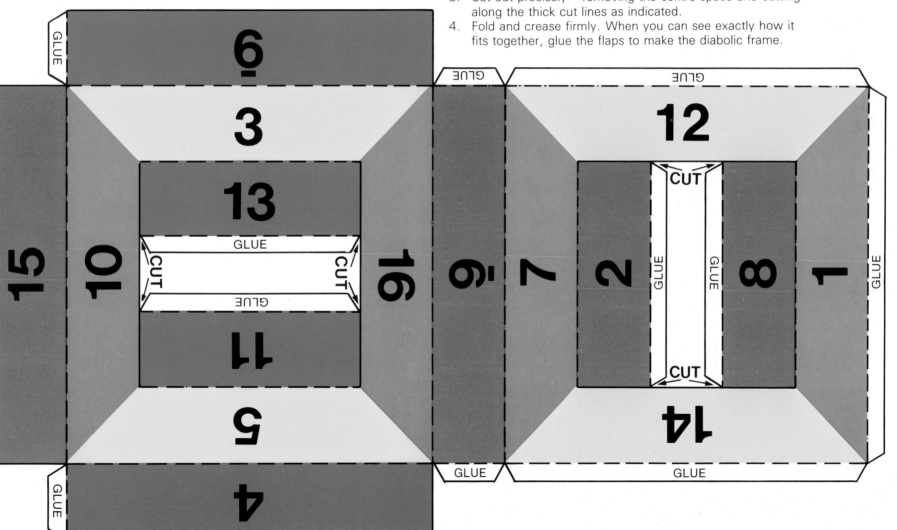

8. The Double Helix

HOW TO MAKE THIS MODEL.
1. Cut out the double helix
2. Score along all the fold lines, solid and dotted.
3. Cut out precisely.
4. Fold and crease firmly. Fold along dotted lines away from you. Fold along solid lines towards you.
5. When all the folds are the correct way you will see the double helix shape develop. Start glueing at one end and then work along to the other.
6. Cut out the rotation protractor and use it to measure the angle of rotation.

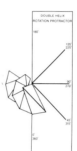

(The protractor in position (showing a rotation of 45°) for one tetrahedron

For more information about the double helix, see page 7 of the minibook.

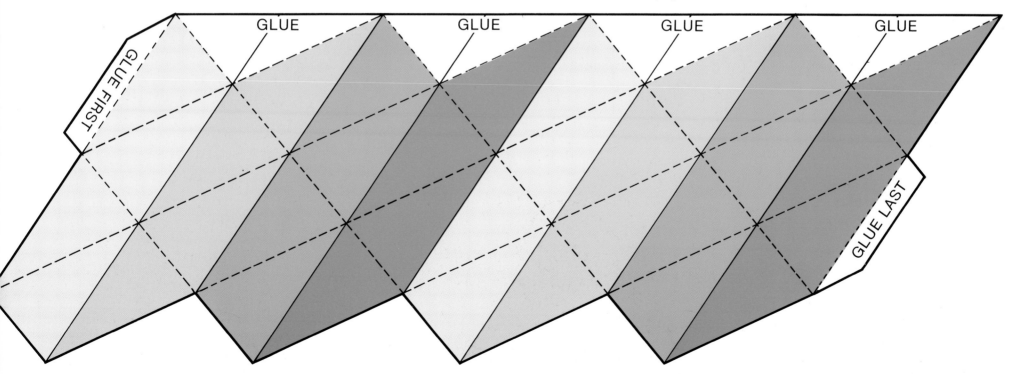

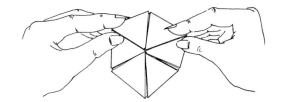

9. A Pair of Hexaflexagons

HOW TO MAKE THESE MODELS.

1. Cut out each model keeping well away from the outline.
2. Score along the central dotted line.
3   Cut out the outline precisely.
4   Fold along the central line away from you and crease firmly. Check that it matches back to back.
5. Spread glue smoothly inside the fold and press tightly.
6. Firmly score all lines and flex backwards and forwards. This helps considerably when the flexagon is complete.
7. Hold the strip so that you are looking at the side without the glue flaps. It does not matter which way up.
8. Fold inwards along the two lines marked — · — · — ·
9. Turn over and fold inwards again along the line marked the same way.
10. This gives a hexagon shape. Complete the hexaflexagon by tucking the flap behind and glueing together the two triangles marked A.

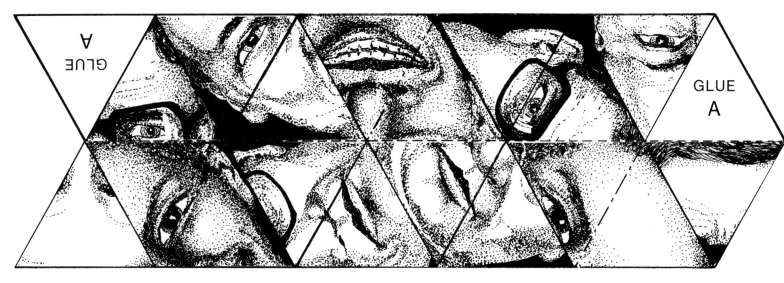

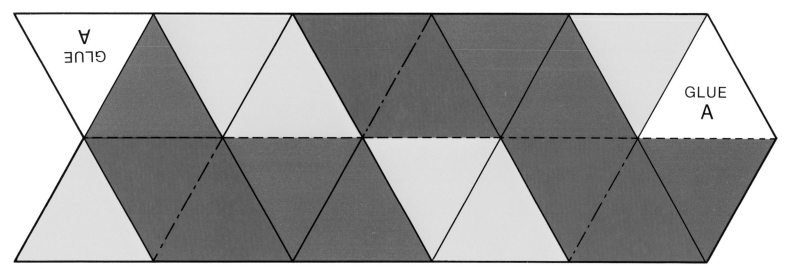

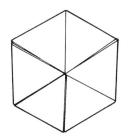

See page 8 of the minibook for more information about Hexaflexagons.

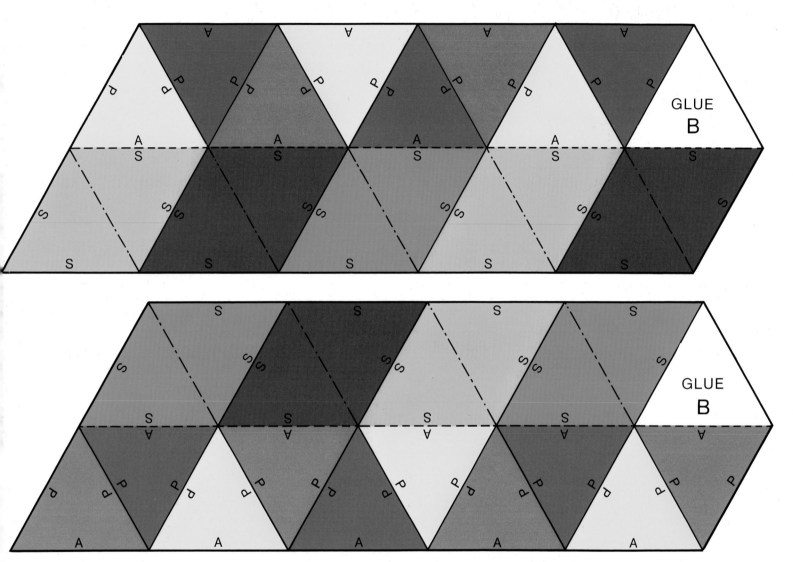

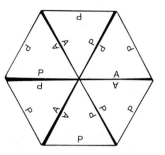

You are strongly advised to make up the simpler hexaflexagons on page 29 first.

HOW TO MAKE THIS MODEL.

1. Cut out each piece and score, fold and glue it back to back as you did for the simpler hexaflexagons on page 29.
2. Glue the two single thickness black triangles together to give one strip 19 triangles long.
3. Looking at the side with the colours green, orange and purple fold inwards on every fold marked —·—·— to give a shorter strip only showing red, blue and yellow.
4. Fold the yellow triangles face to face in order to complete the hexagon.
5. Glue the two "glue" triangles which will come together.

For more information about Hexaflexagons see page 8 of the minibook.

31

Mathematical
Curiosities 1

TARQUIN
PUBLICATIONS

ISBN 0-906212-13-8

9 780906 212134